WINNIE~THE~POO

50 things
to make
the World a
Better
place

EGMONT
We bring stories to life

First published in Great Britain in 2021 by Egmont Books

An imprint of HarperCollins*Publishers*
1 London Bridge Street, London SE1 9GF
www.egmontbooks.co.uk

Parental guidance is advised for all craft and colouring activities. Always ask an grown-up to help
when using glue, paint and scissors. Wear protective clothing and cover surfaces to avoid staining.

MIX
Paper from
responsible sources
FSC™ C007454

This book is produced from independently
certified FSC™ paper to ensure responsible forest management.
For more information visit: www.harpercollins.co.uk/green

Stay safe online. Egmont is not responsible for content hosted by third parties.

Acknowledgments
All images from Dreamstime.com

P 6; ID 72191583 © Wpanyoo, ID 124389937 © Oksana Slepko,ID 178911529 © Nataliia Kozynska, P 7; ID 3591156 © Bidouze Stphane, P 10; ID 79429901 © Studio Grand Web, p 11; ID 49898909 © Tinnakorn Srivichai, p 13; ID 26671474 © Srapulsar38, p 14; ID 183382464 © Zeinousstudio, ID 18188956 © Andersastphoto, ID 8136469 © Melinda Fawver, ID 161342154 © Alexey Lutsenko, ID 15732388 © Plasticrobot, ID 118763870 © Vudhikul Ocharoen, p 15;ID 107239639 © Klavdiia Prokusheva, ID 6442008 © Monkey Business Images, p 17; ID 20037161 © Alexander Shalamov, ID 131832728 © Oleg Prokopenko, ID 62412913 © Rik Trottier, p 18; ID 9418913 © Juan Carlos Tinjaca, p 19; ID 118219466 © Chernetskaya, ID 118116677 © Mangpor2004,p 22; ID 114108207 © Oksun70, ID 920852 © Darren Baker,ID 158054811 © Viktoriia Petrova, P 23; ID 84140023 © Tinnakorn Srivichai, ID 149540937 © Iryna Beldii, ID 116220255 © Dilya Zalyaletdinova, p 24; ID 39467554 © Stockcreations, ID 47241264 © Anekoho, ID 72191583 © Wpanyoo, ID 72794600 © Fortyforks, p 25; ID 156685389 © Golfxx, ID 130478400 © 404045, p 26; ID 162632639 © Amazingmikael, ID 185096471 © Haywiremedia, p 27; ID 26800214 © Nataliia Prokofyeva, ID 178589268 © Julia Kuznetsova, ID 17473179 © Gvictoria, p 28; ID 8422238 © Godfer, ID 53848147 © Rohappy, ID 15864211 © Hongqi Zhang (aka Michael Zhang), ID 174768373 © Millafedotova, ID 15186439 © Homydesign, ID 146199380 © Woodpencil, ID 27927920 © Grafner, ID 22696855 © Filipwarulik, p 31; ID 72340653 © Zoia Lukianova, ID 91710640 © Zoia Lukianova, ID 36737115 © Sarkao, ID 20361815 © Uokhoj, ID 58494420 © Saletomic, ID 7227413 © Robyn Mackenzie, ID 152654935 © Ooliktm, ID 70025908 © Anna Kucherova, p 32; ID 83223722 © Dontree, ID 119821422 © Lightfieldstudiosprod, p 33; ID 2990012 © Onion, ID 72824713 © Margouillat, p 34; ID 54855387 © Svetlana Poselentseva, p 36; ID 116358766 © Soniabonet,ID 78803428 © Draghicich, p 37; ID 192186076 © Natalya Danko, ID 104414788 © Jamakosy, ID 166717702 © Ekaterina Morozova, ID 136551728 © Airdone, p 38; ID 28913900 © Ijacky, ID 90588470 © Supparsorn Wantarnagon, ID 33628796 © Sam74100, p 39; ID 19510691 © Jacek Chabraszewski, p 40; ID 157415652 © Famveldman, ID 25534350 © Diego Vito Cervo, ID 37728502 © Verdateo, ID 152619473 © Dzeinmail, p 41; ID 149841192 © Fizkes, p 43; ID 121582740 © Pavel Kobysh, ID 167662433 © Akesin, ID 6650191 © Kelpfish, ID 111377320 © Elizaveta Galitskaya, ID 95125785 © Chepko, ID 154736822 © Chernetskaya, ID 3499537 © Michael Flippo, p 44; ID 42283405 © Amnachphoto, ID 26671474 © Srapulsar38, ID 70025908 © Anna Kucherova, p 45; ID 70025908 © Anna Kucherova, ID 91204538 © Susanne Neal, ID 20962495 © Simsonne, ID 31605632 © Chris Dorney, ID 145207321 © Syda Productions, ID 44907834 © Wildphotos, p 46; ID 54258817 © Igor Mojzes, ID 167484397 © Serhii Yevdokymov, ID 178069917 © Fizkes, ID 44086027 © Kenishirotie, ID 71923439 © Becky Starsmore, p 47; ID 164242196 © Milkos, ID 182016392 © Serhii Hryshchyshen, ID 158054811 © Viktoriia Petrova, ID 178911529 © Nataliia Kozynska, ID 26671474 © Srapulsar38, p 48; ID 48845897 © Mikhail Rulkov, ID 8906779 © Absoluteindia, p 49; ID 131656513 © Matimix, ID 91319984 © Monkey Business Images, ID 19852108 © Mariusz Blach, p 50; ID 82023232 © Kiankhoon, ID 133948881 © Photka, p 52; ID 177831085 © Lesia Sementsova, ID 113979088 © Hd3dsh, p 54; ID 29684259 © Monkey Business Images, ID 99302860 © Yooran Park, p 55; ID 44926238 © Marjancermelj, p 56; ID 170167362 © William Tobing, ID 175698570 © Wanida Prapan, ID 130478400 © 404045, p 57; ID 57576521 © Kooslin, ID 35325355 © Denys Kuvaiev, p 58; ID 27280438 © Yuryz, p 59; ID 152365542 © Miriam Doerr, ID 152365569 © Miriam Doerr, ID 35307974 © Prestong,p 60; ID 66960228 © Rkpimages, p 61; ID 18269834 © Nico99, ID 71923439 © Becky Starsmore, ID 39844489 © Wildphotos, p 62; ID 34227034 © Andrew Roland, ID 2352667 © Sburel, ID 127833859 © Viacheslav Dubrovin, ID 60524442 © Bestofgreenscreen, p 63; ID 53927757 © Juan Martinez, ID 64615026 © Balatoni Jozsef, ID 66571335 © Natalia Bachkova, ID 110778911 © Elengrant, ID 60524442 © Bestofgreenscreen, p 64; ID 170615211 © Chernetskaya, ID 186539460 © Pakorn Sungkapukdee, ID 170944123 © Photosvit, p 66; ID 26671474 © Srapulsar38, ID 166717702 © Ekaterina Morozova, ID 72191583 © Wpanyoo, ID 42727914 © Jenifoto406, p 67; ID 42727914 © Jenifoto406, ID 37728502 © Verdateo, p 68; ID 27927920 © Grafner, ID 71923439 © Becky Starsmore, ID 70025908 © Anna Kucherova, p 69; ID 6442008 © Monkey Business Images, ID 6650191 © Kelpfish, ID 121582740 © Pavel Kobysh, ID 91204538 © Susanne Neal, p 70; ID 135421437 © Maria Cezara Panaite, ID 71923439 © Becky Starsmore; p 71; ID 166717702 © Ekaterina Morozova, p 72; ID 166717702 © Ekaterina Morozova, p 79; ID 67038578 © Terminator3d, ID 52194507 © Tarikvision

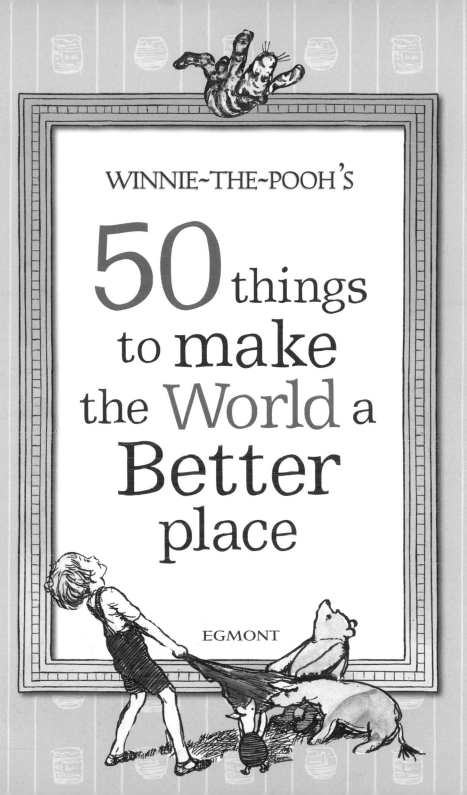

WINNIE~THE~POOH'S

50 things
to **make**
the World a
Better
place

EGMONT

Health and safety

A grown-up may need to help you with some of the things to do in this book. We've let you know on each page if help is needed. And if you're unsure about any of the things to do, always ask!

The
adventures of

. . . .

. . . .

who is making the world
a Better Place

Contents

Tick ✔ each task when you have done it.

It starts with you!

"This is Me!" said Bear, very much surprised … "You were quite right," said Rabbit, looking him all over. "It is you. Glad to see you."

1 Calm breathing

Here's a simple breathing task you can do to relax and clear your mind. All you need is a quiet spot where you can sit comfortably!

Sit cross-legged with your back tall and straight. Close your eyes.

Imagine your tummy is a balloon. Now breathe in deeply to fill the balloon with air.

Breathe out through your nose to release the air from of the balloon. Feel your belly come back in.

Keep breathing in and out. Listen closely to the sound of your breath.

When you're ready, open your eyes, and breathe in and out deeply one more time.

Daily breathing helps you learn about your thoughts and feelings, so you get to know yourself better!

² Listen to your body

Lie flat on your back and close your eyes.

Begin with your toes. Wiggle them around, while keeping the rest of your body still. How do your toes feel today?

Now wiggle your feet. Press them against the ground. How do your feet feel right now?

Move up your body slowly. Wiggle each part one at a time and ask, how does it feel today?

Doing a body scan is a great way to relax and make sure your whole body is feeling good.

3 Live in the moment

Mindfulness is when you focus on what's happening in the moment. If you're feeling worried or upset, take a deep breath and listen to what's happening around you. When you practise paying attention to what's going on and how you feel, you'll be calmer and happier.

We can all make the world a better place by starting with ourselves!

"There's sun on the river and sun on the hill ... You can hear the sea if you stand quite still!"

4 Creative patterns

Colour in the picture on the next page. As you colour focus on the pattern and the colours you choose. Take as much time as you like!

13

5 Mindfulness jar

☆ Start with an empty jar or plastic bottle.

☆ Now add in some biodegradable glitter and then a squeeze of washing up liquid.

☆ Fill the jar with warm water and seal the lid on tightly.

☆ When you are feeling angry or upset, give your mindfulness jar a good shake! Then hold it still and watch the glitter spin round until it slowly stops.

☆ Just like the glitter, your feelings will settle.

We all have strong feelings sometimes! When you feel like that, shake your jar and count to 10 as the glitter swirls.

6 # Celebrate YOU

Make a list of all the things you're good at, no matter how big or small. This is what makes you YOU.

My name is:

This is what I am good at:

Continue your list on page 70.

15

7 Thankfulness list

Take some time to think about lots of good things you are thankful for. It could be anything from having a favourite coloured pencil to your best friend!

You could ask someone to help you write them down or draw them as pictures!

16

8 Start a journal

A journal is a special book to fill with your own thoughts and pictures. You can write about things that have happened to you, or ideas you have. You can draw pictures, too!

Here are some ideas to help you get started:

☆ What was something fun that happened today?

☆ If you could wish for anything, what would it be?

☆ Where is your favourite place to go?

Have a go writing or drawing in your journal every day for a week!

17

9 Write a story

Have you ever wanted to write a story? Here are some ideas to help you get started!

> "Once upon a time, a very long time ago now, about last Friday, Winnie-the-Pooh lived in a forest ..."

Choose a setting. It could be ...

In the forest

On a ship

At the funfair

Choose a character. It could be ...

A dragon

A bear

A turtle

Now it's up to you! What happens next?

10 Book swap

Book swaps are about sharing your favourite books with your friends. And they share theirs with you, too!

It's a wonderful way to share the books you love and learn about new ones!

'What about a **story***?' said Christopher Robin.*

11 Move like Pooh

'SO Round about
And round about
And round about and round about
And round about
I go.'

Moving makes our bodies healthy and strong! Can you copy Winnie-the-Pooh and his friends?

Reach up high, then reach down towards your toes like Pooh.

Leap as far as you can like Kanga.

Skip like **Christopher Robin.**

Walk around on four legs like **Tigger**.

Chase your tail like **Eeyore**.

What other animals can you move like?

12 Stretch it out

Doing yoga every day helps your body relax! You can find somewhere inside your house, or outdoors in your garden or a local park.

Say "good morning" to the sun

Stand up tall and reach both hands up towards the sky. Hello, sun!

Paint a rainbow across the sky

Sit down with your right knee bent and your left leg straight. Reach your right arm up, and sweep it across the sky like you're painting a rainbow! Then switch arms and paint another rainbow on the other side.

Flutter your legs like a butterfly

Sit down, keeping your back very straight. Bend your knees and bring the bottoms of your feet together. Now flap your legs up and down **like a butterfly's wings!**

Pretend to be a tree

Stand still on your left leg. Bend your right knee, and place your right foot just above your left knee. Then repeat on the other side.

Stretch out like a dog

Start with your hands and knees on the floor. Spread your fingers out and plant your palms on the ground. Now slowly straighten your legs as you push your hips up towards the sky.

13 Fun with fruit

Ask a grown-up to help you chop up the fruit.

"What could be more important than a little something to eat?"

Being healthy starts from the inside! Fresh fruit is tasty and colourful ... and it's so good for you, too!

To make fruit kebabs, start with wooden skewers and pieces of fruit. You can use grapes, berries, bananas, melon or any other fruit.

Carefully push each piece of fruit onto the skewer. Yum! Yum!

You could even make cut-out shapes of fruit, like triangles or stars!

14 Keeping Fresh

Water is refreshing and helps keeps your body and mind in tip-top shape.
Drink 4 glasses water every day for a week. Why not add ice cubes or frozen fruit too?

Reuseable bottles or cups are better for the environment than plastic ones!

15 Learn about water

Where does your tap water come from? Depending on where you live, it may come from the ground, from a river or even from rainwater! Ask an adult to help you look up where you get your fresh water.

16 Explore your senses

We use our senses to explore the world around us.
Try these games to focus on each of your senses in turn.

Hearing

Find somewhere comfortable outside to sit down. Close your eyes and listen. What sounds do you hear? Now cup your hand around your ear. Can you hear more or less this way?

Seeing

Look up at the sky and say three things you see.
Look down at the ground and say three things you see.

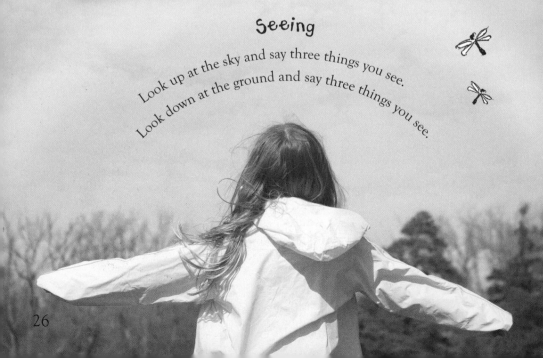

Tasting

Ask a grown-up to help you gather a spoonful of honey, a slice of lemon and one crisp. Now taste each one. Which tastes salty? Which tastes sweet? Which tastes sour?

These are suggestions. Why not choose your favourite foods!

Smelling

Put on a blindfold or close your eyes tightly. Ask a grown-up to bring you three things with strong smells. Can you guess what they are just by sniffing?

Ask a grown-up to help you with these experiments.

Touching

Ask a grown-up to put five things inside an empty bag or pillowcase. Reach in and feel each one. Can you guess what they are? No peeking!

27

17 Say "Hello" in five languages

*'Hallo, Piglet,' said Pooh.
'Hallo, Pooh,' said Piglet, 'I knew it was you.'
'So did I," said Pooh.*

Here are five different ways to say "hello"!

French: **Bonjour!**
Say: "Bohn-zhoor!"

Spanish: **Hola**
Say: "Oh-la!"

German: **Guten-tag**
Say: "Goo-ten tahg!"

Japanese: **Konnichiwa**
Say: "Cone-ee-chee-wah!"

Vietnamese: **Xin Chào**
Say: "Zeen chow!"

What other greetings do you know?

Fun things with old things

'We will build it here,' said Pooh. '
We will build an Eeyore House with sticks.'
So they got down off the gate and went round
to the other side of the wood to fetch the sticks.

18 Make a Useful Pot

"You can keep anything in it," said Pooh.
"It's Very Useful like that."

Upcycling is taking something that you would have thrown away and turning it into something new! It's very good for the planet, and it's super fun and creative!

You can make your own Useful Pots, just like Pooh and his friends! First, wash up old jam jars or honey pots so they're nice and clean. Use your favourite acrylic paints to give the jar a base colour and let it dry.

Then it's time to get creative! Be careful not to make too much mess when decorating. Here are some ideas:

☆ Paint a picture or dotty pattern on the jar

☆ Tie a ribbon or piece of cloth around the jar

☆ Add stickers all over the jar

☆ Make a pretty collage by gluing buttons or scraps of felt on the jar

Eeyore keeps his birthday
present in his Useful Pot.
Here are some things you
could put in your Useful Pots:

☆ Pencils, crayons
   or paintbrushes

☆ Pretty pebbles or shells

☆ Flowers

☆ Coins

19 Board game

If you save old bottle caps, you'll soon have enough to make your own board game!

☆ To make a noughts and crosses game, start by painting an X on five bottle caps, and an O on another five. You could also paint your caps two different colours!

☆ To make the board, take a big piece of paper. Draw two long lines going top-to-bottom, and two long lines going side-to-side.

☆ Once the paint on the bottle caps dries, you're ready to play. Take it in turns to place a bottle cap on the board. The first person to get three of their caps in a row in any direction wins!

What other games could you play with old bottle caps?

20 Tin-can shaker

You can make a wonderful musical shaker with a tin can, an old sock, and an elastic band. Make sure to ask a grown-up to help you as tin cans can have sharp edges!

Step 1:
As a grown-up to rinse out an empty tin can.

Step 2:
Being careful of the sharp edges, pour a handful of dried rice inside the tin.

Step 3:
Ask a grown-up to pull a sock over the tin can and use an elastic band to hold it in place. This will keep the dried rice inside the tin.

Step 4:
Now your shaker is ready for you to dance along to the music!

You could try adding small pebbles or dried lentils instead of rice for a different sound!

21 Reusable shopping bag

Follow these instructions to
make a reusable shopping bag
from a t-shirt. All you need is an
old t-shirt and a pair of scissors.
Make sure you ask a grown-up
to help you!

1 First, cut the sleeves
off the t-shirt.

2 Next, cut out the
neckline area. This
shape will become
the handles.

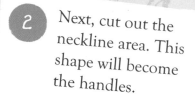

3 Now, turn the t-shirt inside-out. Cut a fringe along the bottom. Each strip should be about 10cm long, 1.5cm wide.

Ask a grown-up to help you!

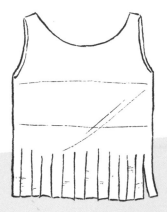

4 Tie each strip to the strip behind it. Then make a second row of knots by tying each strip to the strip next to it. Tie a double-knot at each end.

5 Lastly, turn the shirt outside-in. Now you have a lovely, reusable bag!

22 Egg carton rabbits

*"I walked on the common
The old-gold common...
And I saw little rabbits
'Most everywhere!"*

To make little rabbits, you will need a recycled egg carton, scissors, glue and paint or marker pens.

☆ Ask a grown-up to help you cut up the egg carton. You will need one egg cup for each rabbit. Then cut two ears from the top of the box or you can use a sheet of card.

☆ Use markers or paint to add bunny faces: eyes, nose, mouth and whiskers!

☆ Then decorate the ears.

☆ Finally, glue the ears on the back to create your rabbits!

36

23 Kitchen roll honeybees

Ask a grown-up to help you!

These buzzy bees will keep you busy! You'll need an empty kitchen roll tube, paint, scissors and glue.

1 Cut your kitchen roll tube in half. This will give you bodies for two bees.

2 Paint the body bright yellow. Let it dry. Then paint black stripes around the body. Let the stripes dry.

3 Cut out the head, antennae and wings on page 71. Or you can trace the shape on your own sheets of coloured paper.

4 Use paint or markers to decorate the face. Then glue the antennae to the head.

5 Build your bee by gluing the wings on the back of the body, and the head to the front of the body. Buzz!

 "If there's a buzzing-noise, someone's making a buzzing-noise, and the only reason for making a buzzing-noise that I know of is because you're a bee."

24 Brilliant bookmarks!

Ask a grown-up to help you cut out the characters.

If you save your ice-lolly sticks, you can turn them into bookmarks!

- ☆ First, wash the ice-lolly stick.

- ☆ Next, ask a grown-up to help you cut out the characters from page 73 of this book. Or you can make your own designs!

- ☆ Glue the character onto the back of a recycled cereal box, or any piece of card.

- ☆ When the glue is dried, carefully cut out your design.

- ☆ Lastly, glue your character onto the ice-lolly stick. Now your bookmark is ready. What is your favourite book?

It's fun to be kind

"She knew at once that, however **BIG** Tigger seemed to be, he wanted as much *kindness* as Roo."

Kindness is thinking about other people and their feelings. Being kind is nice for the other person, and makes you feel good, too. There are many different ways to practise kindness!

25 Smile

A **big smile** can brighten someone else's day – and your own!

26 Make someone laugh

You can tell a joke or funny story, or even make a silly face.

27 Say thank you

Think of someone who has done something nice for you. It could be a family member or friend, or someone in your neighbourhood.

Say "thank you", and be sure to tell them why you are thanking them!

'Eeyore,' said Pooh solemnly, 'I, Winnie-the-Pooh, will find your tail for you.' 'Thank you, Pooh,' answered Eeyore. 'You're a real friend.'

Ask a grown-up to cut out the thank-you notes on page 75.

28 Write thank-you notes

Choose four people and write them a note, thanking them for something they have done. You could give them the note in person or leave it somewhere for them to find as a surprise!

Thank you

Thank you

"Oh, Bear!" said Christopher Robin.
"How I do love you!"
"So do I," said Pooh.

29 Celebrate your friend

What is your best friend really good at? Make a list of five things you like about them. Then share the list, to show them how lucky you are to have them for a friend!

Or why not draw a picture of you and your friend together!

30 Get to know someone better

Ask someone five questions about themselves. It shows that you are interested and you will learn more about them!

Here are some questions to get you started:

☆ What is your favourite food?

☆ What do you like to do on rainy days?

☆ What is your favourite song?

☆ What was the last party you went to?

☆ What is your favourite animal?

What other questions could you ask?

43

31 Friendship box

To make a friendship box, start with a small box, like a shoebox. Decorate it with pens, paint, stickers or colourful scraps of paper. You could even write your friend's name on top.

Now fill the box with things that make you think of your friend.

Here are some ideas to put in your friendship box:

- ☆ A painted rock or seashell
- ☆ A small drawing of something you did together
- ☆ A note
- ☆ Tasty treats

Why not wrap the box in wrapping paper and give it to your friend!

32 Write a letter

"Soft words of comfort and of cheer."

Grab some paper and pencils or crayons and write a letter to your grandparents, your parents or one of your friends. A small message can brighten someone's day! You could decorate the envelope with marker pens, too.

Here are some ideas to get started:

☆ Begin with 'Dear Friend'

☆ Let them know you are thinking of them

☆ Draw a picture or write about something that makes you happy

☆ Sign your first name

If you don't want to write, why not draw a picture!

33 Window decorations

Window decorations are sure to lift the spirits of anyone who walks past your house.

First, find a big piece of paper. Then get creative! Use paint, crayons or markers to make your window decoration as bright and colourful as you can.

Tape your finished artwork inside the window, facing out so everyone can see it.

Remember: the bigger and brighter your art, the more it shows up in your window!

Why not make:

☆ A rainbow

☆ A shining sun

☆ A page of colourful dots or shapes

34 Donate a toy

"A little Consideration, a little Thought for Others, makes all the difference."

Some children don't have lots of toys to play with. You can help by donating one of your toys to charity for another child to enjoy. Make sure to ask an adult to help you with this task!

Choose a toy that you don't play with as much anymore, and make sure it's still in good condition.

Look for a local shelter, hospital or children's centre that accepts used toys.

Donate your toy to someone new!

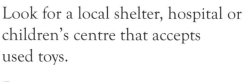

35 Do a charity challenge

Pick a charity that's important to you. Your charity may have organised events like a race or a bake sale. You can also come up with your own challenge and donate all the money you've raised.

Ask a grown-up to help you get ready.

Let your family and friends know that you are fundraising. Ask them nicely if they will sponsor you. Remember to let everyone know how your challenge went!

To get you started, there's a sponsor sheet on page 79.

36 Help someone

Offer to help a grown-up or brother or sister with a chore. By working together, the job will be finished sooner.

If you're not sure what to do, ask them: "How can I help you today?"

"It is the best way to write poetry, letting things come."

37 Share a poem

Write a poem to share with someone. Poetry can make us feel good, and there are many types of poems!

Choose one from the ideas below or come up with one of your own.

Begin by writing a word or name vertically on the page. Now write one line for each letter.

True stripy friend

Is always there.

Good at jumping,

Great at bouncing,

Excellent fun,

Really big smile.

Write a poem that rhymes.

Isn't it funny
How a bear likes honey?

Write whatever comes into your mind! It can be as many lines as you like, and it doesn't have to rhyme.

OWL, WOL to some
Never LOW, always HIGH
High in the trees.
High in the Sky.
That's Owl.

Read your poem out loud a few times to practise.
Then share it with someone you love!

38 Food packages

Some families and children don't have enough food to eat. You can put a food package together and take it to a foodbank to help families who are hungry.

Collect foods that can be stored for a long time. You can ask your local foodbank what foods they'd like most.

Make sure to ask a grown-up if it's OK to donate your chosen foods!

HERE ARE SOME IDEAS:

Tinned fruits or vegetables

Dried pasta or rice

Tinned soup

Cereal

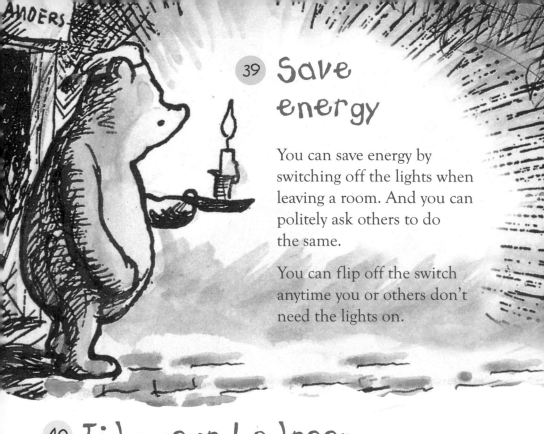

39 Save energy

You can save energy by switching off the lights when leaving a room. And you can politely ask others to do the same.

You can flip off the switch anytime you or others don't need the lights on.

40 Tidy your bedroom

Put away any toys or books on the floor. When you treat your things nicely, they last much longer!

The world around us

"If you were a bird, and lived on high,
  You'd lean on the wind when the wind came by,
You'd say to the wind when it took you away:
'That's where I wanted
  to go to-day!'"

The Earth is our home,
and it's up to us to protect our home
and take good care of it!

Always pick up litter with a grown-up. Never pick anything up you don't recognise!

41 Litter picker

The best way to show you love the planet is to look after it. Help keep the Earth clean and safe for everyone!

Ask a grown-up to come with you and choose a place to go for a walk. It can be a local park, or even on your street. Put on a pair of gloves, and if you see a piece of litter, pick it up! Can you collect five pieces of litter and put them in the bin?

Picking up litter helps keep our streets and parks clean, and stops animals getting hurt.

42 Bug hotel

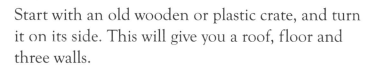

You can make a home for
bugs and give them a safe place to stay.

Start with an old wooden or plastic crate, and turn
it on its side. This will give you a roof, floor and
three walls.

Now build the bug bedrooms by stacking rows of sturdy
tins (like empty cans of beans). Ask a grown-up to help
you with tins as they can have sharp edges!

For the bedding, fill the tin cans
with moss, bark, straw, pine cones,
bamboo, sticks or dry leaves.
The more materials you use,
the more types of animals will
want to stay.

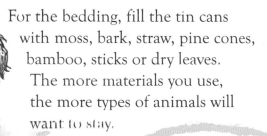

A grown-up can help you
make an even bigger bug
hotel if you have planks of
wood or old bricks to build
the structure.

43 Plastic planters

You will need old plastic bottles and some seeds or herbs! You can get these at your local supermarket.

Take the empty plastic bottle and lay it on its side. Ask a grown-up to cut a wide section out of the top.

Put a layer of potting soil on the bottom. Make sure you have at least 3cm gap between the top of the soil and the opening in your planter. Then plant your favourite flowers or herbs and watch them grow!

Make sure your seeds are covered in a couple of cms of soil once they are planted!

44 Collect rainwater

The next time it rains, ask a grown-up to you put a bucket or barrel outside to gather rainwater. You can use the raindrops you've collected for watering your plants.

45 Milk bottle watering can

Did you know you can make your own watering can?

☆ First save a plastic milk bottle.

☆ Rinse it out and dry it.

☆ Then decorate the bottle with paint or scraps of fabric and glue.

☆ Unscrew the lid and ask a grown-up to poke holes through the lid, with a hammer and nail. These are your holes for watering!

☆ Now fill the bottle with water and screw the lid on tightly. It's time to water your plants!

46 Mini pond

A mini pond can become a home for wildlife. Ask a grown-up to help you make a mini-pond in your garden or even on your windowsill.

☆ You'll need a water-tight container to start. This could be a bowl or an old tub!

☆ Put a layer of sand or gravel at the bottom (2.5cm deep). Then add a few bigger rocks or old bricks.

☆ Fill the container with rainwater and place it outside.

☆ Remember to keep checking on your pond to see if any animals have moved in!

Keep an eye out for wildlife: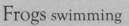

Frogs swimming

Birds taking a bath

Dragonflies laying their eggs

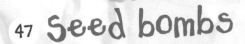

47 Seed bombs

CLAY MIX

A seed bomb is a ball of seeds you can plant anywhere you like! Start with a large mixing bowl. Add:

- ☆ 1 cup of potting soil or compost   SOIL
- ☆ 2 cups of pottery clay mix
- ☆ 1 cup of water
- ☆ 1 cup of seeds   SEEDS

Mix everything together with your hands. It's ok to get messy!

Roll the mixture into balls 5cm wide. Leave the seed bombs somewhere warm to dry.

Plant your seed bombs by throwing them into an open green space ... and then wait and see what grows!

You can find pottery clay mix at your local crafts shop.

48 Animal expert

Read about different types of animals and tick ✔ when you spot one!

Mammals

Mammals have hair on their bodies, and all baby mammals drink milk. Here are some mammals you might see.

- ◯ Dogs
- ◯ Cats
- ◯ Rabbits
- ◯ Foxes

Birds

Birds hatch from eggs and they are covered in feathers. Most birds can fly, but not all. Here are some birds you might see.

- ◯ Ducks
- ◯ Swans
- ◯ Chickens
- ◯ Robins

Fish

Fish live in the water. They have fins for swimming and gills so they can breathe underwater. Here are some fish you might see.

- ◯ Cod
- ◯ Bass
- ◯ Salmon
- ◯ Plaice

Insects

Insects are small animals with six legs. Most insects also have wings and antennae. Here are some insects you might see.

- ○ Beetles
- ○ Ladybirds
- ○ Butterflies
- ○ Bees

Reptiles

Reptiles have dry, scaly skin instead of hair or feathers. They are born on land. Here are some reptiles you might see.

- ○ Lizards
- ○ Snakes
- ○ Turtles
- ○ Legless Lizard

Amphibians

Amphibians are born in the water but move to the land when they grow up. Here are some amphibians you might see.

- ○ Frogs
- ○ Toads
- ○ Newts
- ○ Tadpoles

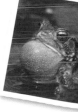

49 Nature journal

To make your very own nature journal, find a blank notebook or ask a grown-up to help you staple pieces of paper together.

Decorate the cover. You could write your name on, too.

Use your nature journal to observe the world around you – in your home, in your garden, at the park or at a farm.

Pay attention to what is happening outside:

What season is it?

What is the weather like?

What insects do you see?

What birds sounds can you hear?

What plants are blooming in the park?

What flowers can you smell?

What else do you see?
Write or draw what
you spot each time!

50 Screen-free day

Choose a date to have a screen-free day, then write it in your diary so you don't forget.

Here are some things you can do without a screen. You may come up with more ideas of your own!

☆ Play outside

☆ Go for a walk or bike ride

☆ Cook something with a grown-up

☆ Read a story

☆ Paint a picture

☆ Build a fort

☆ Try some of the things in this book

Well done!

Every day you have a new chance
to make the world a better place!

How did you do?

I was given this book by:

The most fun activity was:

Something I tried for the first time was:

I did this activity with my friend:

The activity that made me
think the most was:

Gallery

Stick photos or draw
pictures of your favourite
activities here.

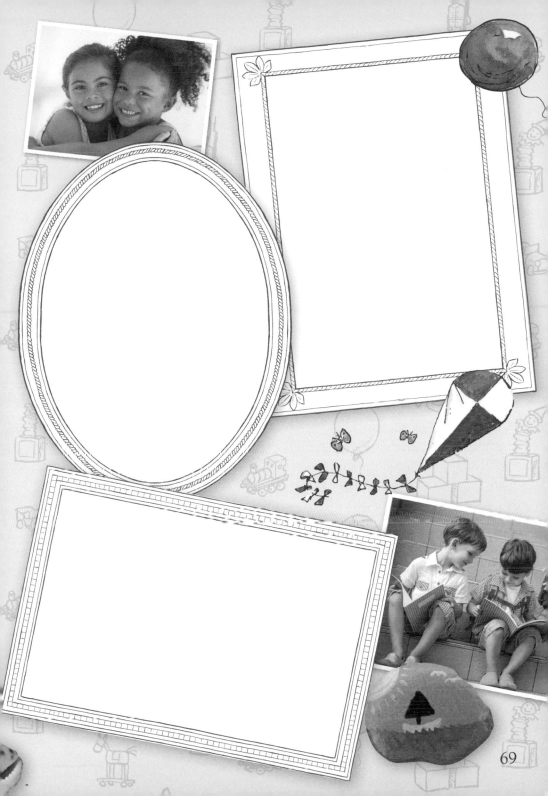

Here are more things I'm good at:

You can continue your list here from page 15

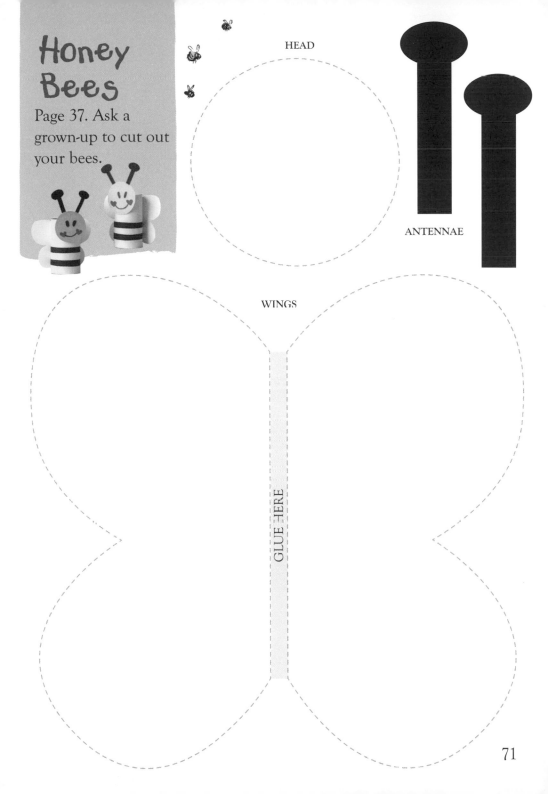

Honey Bees

Page 37. Ask a grown-up to cut out your bees.

HEAD

ANTENNAE

WINGS

GLUE HERE

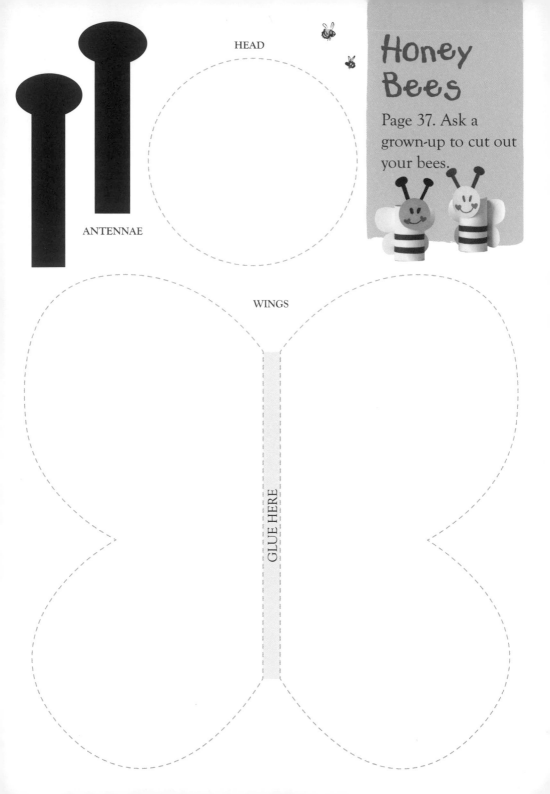

ANTENNAE

HEAD

WINGS

GLUE HERE

Honey Bees

Page 37. Ask a grown-up to cut out your bees.

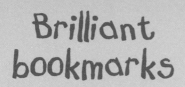

Brilliant bookmarks

Ask a grown-up to help you trace or cut out this page. Then cut out the characters for the bookmark activity on page 38.

Brilliant bookmarks

Ask an grown-up to help you trace or cut out this page. Then cut out the characters for the bookmark activity on page 38.

Thank you

From

. . . .

. . . .

From

. . . .

. . . .

Thank you

CUT ALONG BLACK DOTTED LINE

To

Thank you for

. . . .

. . . .

. . . .

. . . .

. . . .

. . . .

To

Thank you for

. . . .

. . . .

. . . .

. . . .

. . . .

. . . .

From

. . . .

. . . .

Thank you

CUT ALONG **BLACK** DOTTED LINE

Thank
you

From

. . . .

. . . .

FOLD ALONG **BLUE** DOTTED LINE

To

· ·

· ·

Thank you for

· ·

· ·

· ·

· ·

· ·

To

· ·

· ·

Thank you for

· ·

· ·

· ·

· ·

· ·